EXODUS

Brian Wildsmith

THE TEN COMMANDMENTS

I AM YOUR GOD.

I RESCUED YOU FROM EGYPT WHERE YOU LIVED AS SLAVES.

YOU MUST NOT WORSHIP ANY OTHER GODS.
YOU MUST NOT MAKE ANY IDOLS OR IMAGES TO WORSHIP.
YOU MUST NOT USE MY NAME WRONGFULLY.
YOU MUST NOT WORK ON THE SABBATH DAY.

YOU MUST HONOR YOUR FATHER AND MOTHER.

YOU MUST NOT KILL.

YOU MUST NOT TAKE SOMEONE ELSE'S HUSBAND OR WIFE.

YOU MUST NOT STEAL.

YOU MUST NOT ACCUSE ANYONE UNJUSTLY.

YOU MUST NOT COVET THINGS THAT BELONG TO OTHER PEOPLE.

First published in 1998
in the United Kingdom by Oxford University Press
and in 1999 in the United States of America
by Eerdmans Books for Young Readers

This edition published by arrangement with
Oxford University Press for distribution via PJ Library
only throughout UK, USA, Canada and Australia

Manufactured in China
032031.9K2/B0800/A8

ISBN 9780192746320

EXODUS
Brian Wildsmith

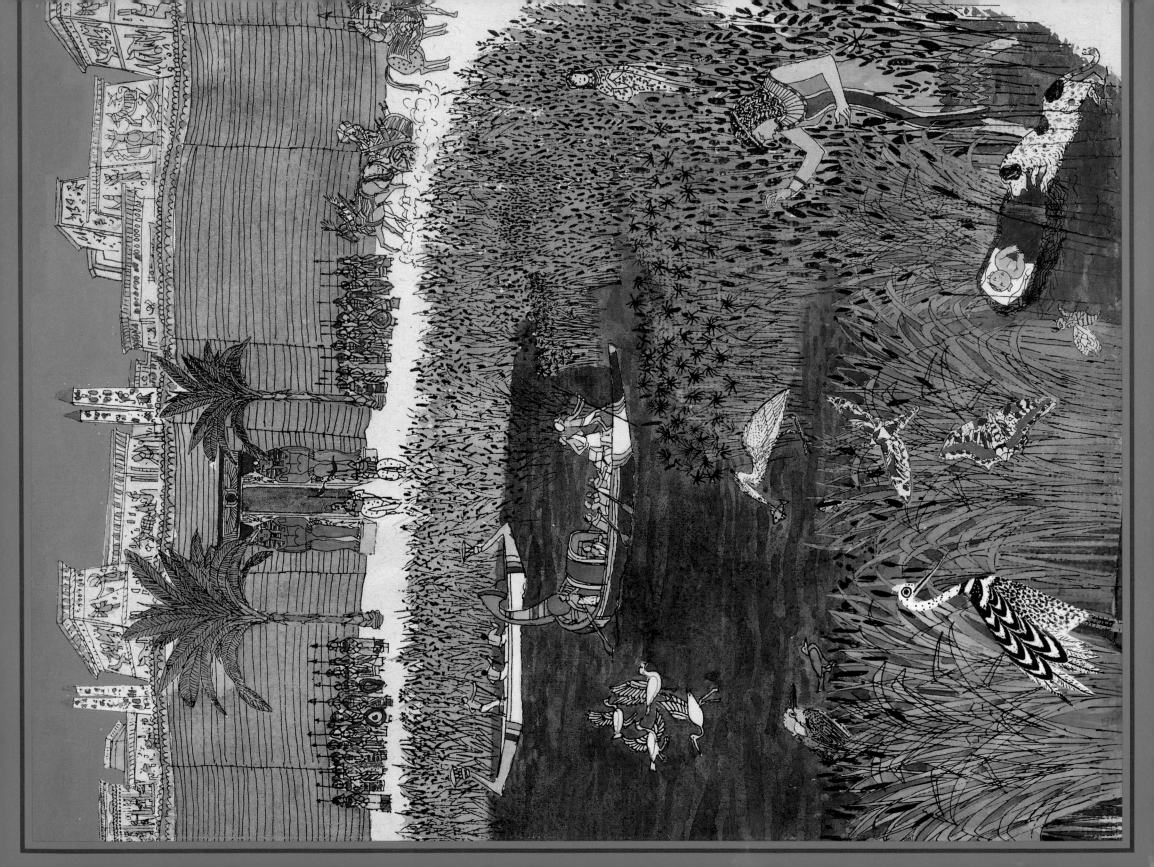

When the Hebrews were slaves in Egypt, a Hebrew woman gave birth to a son. Now Pharaoh had ordered that all the Hebrew baby boys should be killed. The mother made a basket of reeds, placed her baby inside, and hid it among the bullrushes. Her daughter Miriam kept watch nearby.

Some time later Pharaoh's daughter came down to the river to bathe. She heard the baby crying and picked him up. She felt sorry for the little boy.

Miriam came forward and asked, "Shall I go and find one of the Hebrew women to nurse the child for you?"

So Miriam fetched the baby's mother. Pharaoh's daughter said, "Look after this little boy for me, and I will pay you."

The woman took the baby and nursed him. When he was old enough, she brought him back to Pharaoh's daughter, who named him Moses.

Moses grew up as an Egyptian prince, surrounded by the riches of Egypt. But he never forgot that he was a Hebrew, and he hated the cruel way his people were treated.

One day he saw an Egyptian guard whipping a Hebrew slave. Moses was so angry that he leaped at the guard and killed him with his bare hands.

When Pharaoh heard of this, he was very angry and wanted to kill Moses. He summoned the captain of the guard and ordered him to arrest Moses.

But Moses fled to the land of Midian, where he lived and worked as a shepherd for many years.

In time Pharaoh died and was replaced by another king. The new Pharaoh was just as cruel, and the Hebrews in Egypt suffered even more than before.

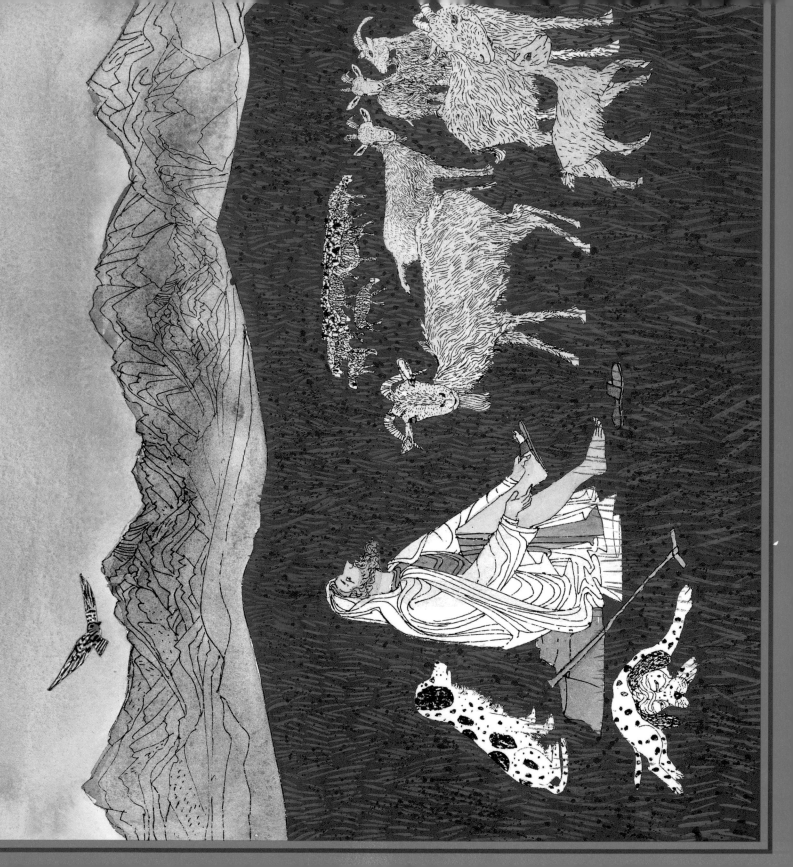

One day while Moses was looking after his flock in Midian, God appeared to him as a fire blazing out from a bush. Although the bush was on fire, it was not burned up.

God called to Moses from out of the flames and said, "Take off your shoes, for you are standing on holy ground. I am your God, and I have seen the suffering of my people. Go back to Egypt and tell Pharaoh to let my people go. You will lead them out of Egypt to a land flowing with milk and honey."

Then God spoke to Moses' brother, Aaron, in Egypt, and said, "Your brother is coming home. Go and meet him."

The two brothers met and went to Pharaoh's court together. They said to Pharaoh, "The Lord God has sent us to tell you to set the Hebrews free and let them leave Egypt."

"I do not know your God," replied Pharaoh. "Can your God show me a sign?"

Then Aaron threw his staff to the ground, and it turned into a snake. When Pharaoh called his magicians to throw down their staffs, their staffs also became snakes. But Aaron's snake swallowed up all of their snakes.

Pharaoh took no notice. "No," he said. "I will not let your people go."

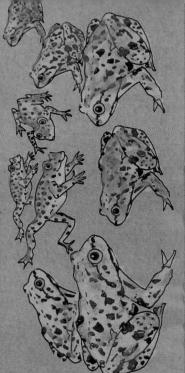

So God sent a series of plagues to strike Egypt. The Nile River turned to blood, and the country was invaded by frogs, insects, and flies. The cattle died, and boils covered the people's bodies. Fierce hailstorms raged, locusts ate up all the corn, and God sent darkness for three days. Still Pharaoh would not let the Hebrews go.

Finally God said to Moses, "Tonight the eldest son of each family in the land will die, but you and your people will be safe if you do as I command." So each Hebrew family killed a lamb and painted its blood on their doorposts.

They roasted the lamb, ate it with flat bread and bitter herbs, and waited while the angel of death passed over them. Hebrews still remember this time and celebrate it with a feast called Passover.

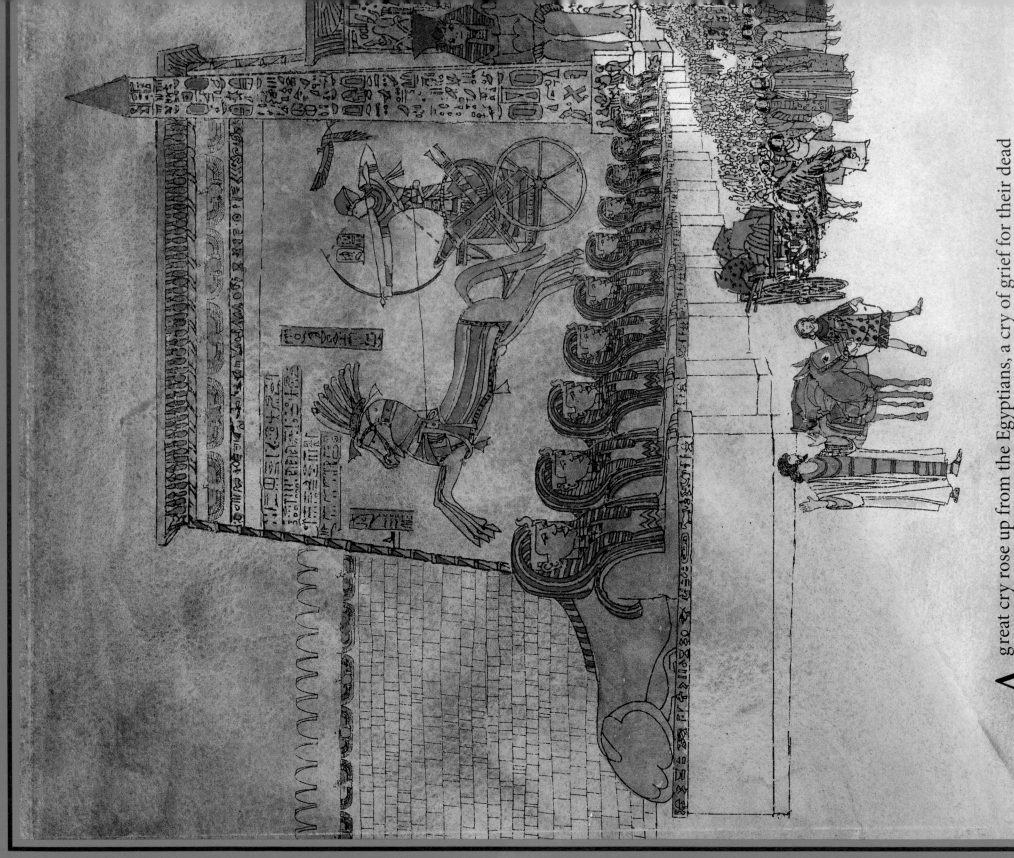

A great cry rose up from the Egyptians, a cry of grief for their dead sons. Then Pharaoh summoned Moses and Aaron to him and said, "Leave this land, you and all your people. Leave, or we shall all be dead!"

The Hebrews left Egypt that night, more than six hundred thousand men, together with women and children and their flocks and cattle. Moses led the way, and a young boy named Joshua walked by his side.

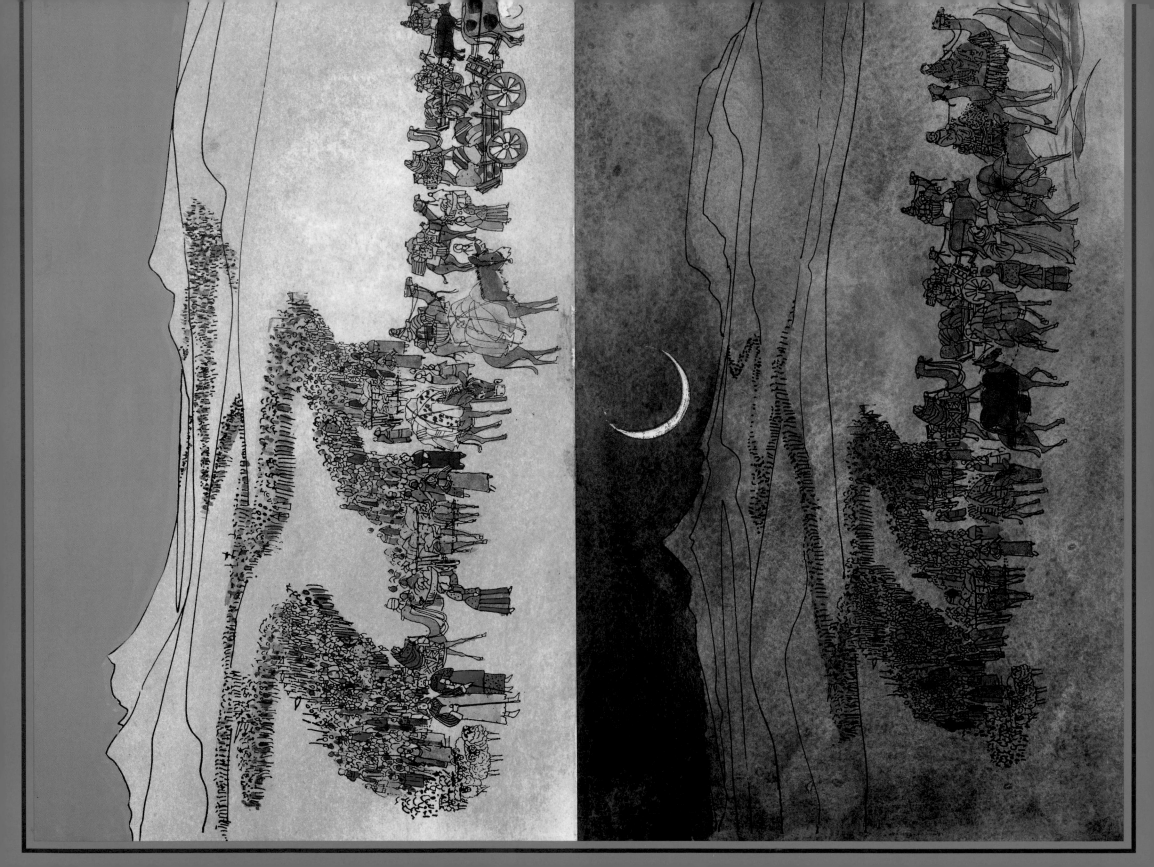

God led the Hebrews in a pillar of cloud by day and guided them by a pillar of flame during the night.

But Pharaoh changed his mind and sent his chariots after the Hebrew people. When the Egyptians caught up with them, the Hebrews had reached the Red Sea. God caused the pillar of cloud to bring darkness on the Egyptians and the pillar of flame to bring light to the Hebrews. So the two armies were kept apart.

Then God sent a powerful east wind, which parted the waters in two. The Hebrews walked through the middle of the sea on dry ground and crossed safely to the other side. When the Egyptians tried to follow, the sea came roaring down on them and swept them away.

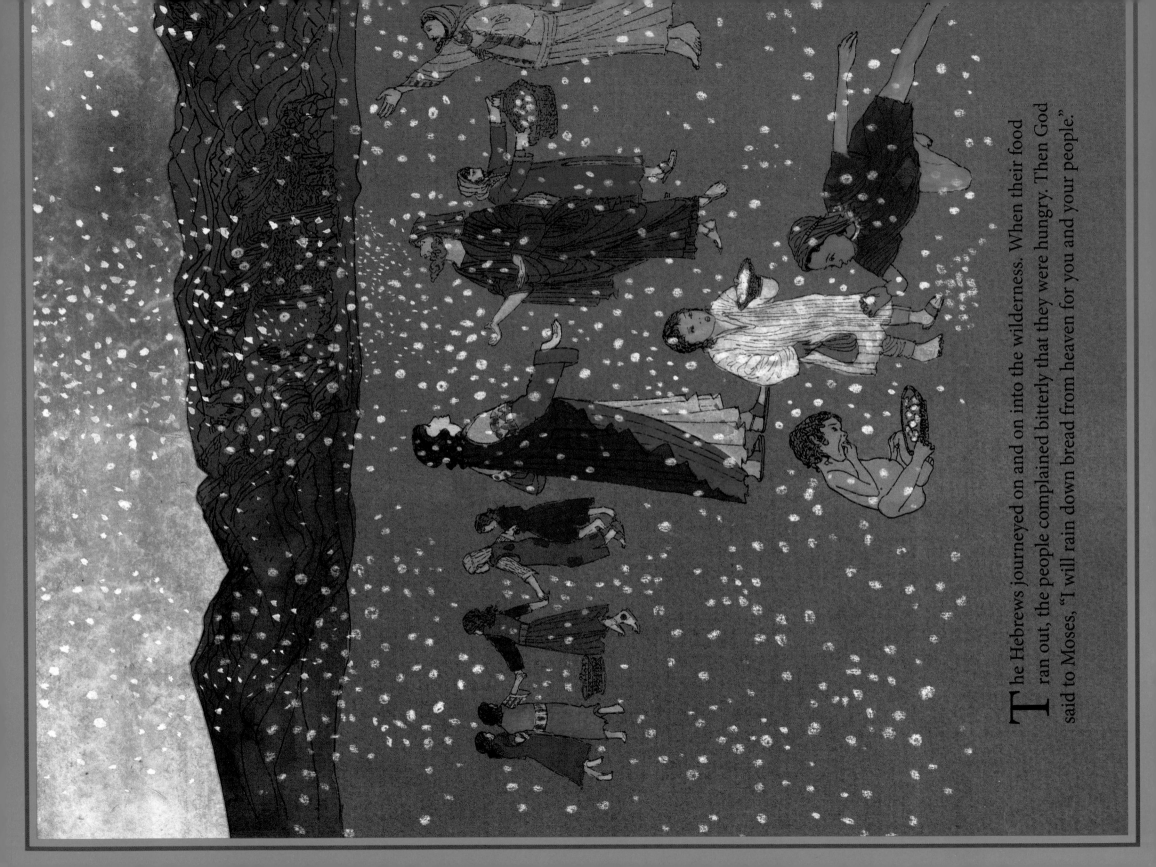

The Hebrews journeyed on and on into the wilderness. When their food ran out, the people complained bitterly that they were hungry. Then God said to Moses, "I will rain down bread from heaven for you and your people."

The next day, in the early morning, God covered the ground with food. It was white and tasted o~ honey, and Moses called it manna. All the time that the Hebrews were in the desert, God gave them manna to eat.

God also sent them flocks of birds called quails, which they cooked and ate.

A s the Hebrews went deeper into
the desert, the sun beat down on
them, and there was no water. They began
to quarrel with Moses. "We should have stayed
in Egypt!" they cried. "We will all die of thirst here."
God told Moses to strike a rock with his staff. Suddenly fresh water
gushed out, and they all had enough to drink.

After walking for three months, the Hebrews came to the foot of Mount Sinai. There God called out for Moses to come to meet him. So Moses went up to the top of the mountain, amid thunder and lightning, flames of fire and the blast of trumpets. Then God gave Moses the Ten Commandments, written on two tablets of stone. These laws told the people how they should live.

Moses stayed on the mountain for so long that the people grew angry and impatient. They shouted at Aaron, "What happened to Moses? Where is his God now? Make us another god, a god that we can see." So Aaron collected their golden jewelry, melted it down, and made them a golden calf.

When Moses returned, the people were dancing and worshiping the golden calf. Moses was so angry that he broke the tablets God had given him and destroyed the golden calf.

But God forgave the people and ordered Moses to cut two new tablets of stone. Moses carried them up the mountain, and God wrote out the Ten Commandments again.

When Moses came down, his face was shining because he had been talking with God. And all the people listened as Moses taught them the laws of God.

For forty years the Hebrews made their way through the wilderness until at last they reached the edge of the Jordan valley. From the top of a high mountain God showed Moses the beautiful land of Canaan. "This is the land I promised to give to my people," God said. "I have let you see it from a distance, but you shall not enter it."

And there Moses died. His people buried him in a peaceful valley, and they wept for him for thirty days.

Then Joshua, who had first followed Moses when he was a boy, took his place and led the Hebrews into the promised land.

After all their wanderings and struggles, they were a free people at last. They had finally come home.

THE TEN COMMANDMENTS

I AM YOUR GOD.

I RESCUED YOU FROM EGYPT WHERE YOU LIVED AS SLAVES.

YOU MUST NOT WORSHIP ANY OTHER GODS.
YOU MUST NOT MAKE ANY IDOLS OR IMAGES TO WORSHIP.
YOU MUST NOT USE MY NAME WRONGFULLY.
YOU MUST NOT WORK ON THE SABBATH DAY.

YOU MUST HONOR YOUR FATHER AND MOTHER.
YOU MUST NOT KILL.
YOU MUST NOT TAKE SOMEONE ELSE'S HUSBAND
OR WIFE.
YOU MUST NOT STEAL.
YOU MUST NOT ACCUSE ANYONE UNJUSTLY.
YOU MUST NOT COVET THINGS THAT BELONG
TO OTHER PEOPLE.

ENGAGING CHILDREN WITH PASSOVER

Here are some suggestions to make Passover memorable and fun for your children. (Remember, there's no one right way to celebrate the holiday.)

✡ First, be prepared to enjoy Passover. Your children will react to your mood of pleasure and playfulness.

✡ Traditionally, the person leading the *seder* reclines on a pillow to signify the ease of being a free person. Anyone who chooses can have such a pillow. Encourage your children to use paint or fabric pens to give a Passover theme to a plain pillowcase. At the seder, be sure to give credit for the fabulous results.

✡ Recipes fascinate some children. Let your children help choose a new food to introduce at the seder. *Charoset*, the fragrant mixture symbolic of the mortar used by the Hebrew slaves, lends itself especially well to variations.

✡ A Passover play may be in your future. In advance of the holiday, encourage your children to choose a portion of the Passover story and act it out with siblings and/or friends. Help them get creative with costumes and props. Their play might even be presented at the seder!

✡ Consider having a child's version of a *Haggadah* (the text used by seder participants) at the seder. Give all children who are able a chance to read a few sentences from it. Be sure to let them rehearse in advance so they'll feel comfortable.

✡ Encourage the important Jewish tradition of asking questions. As the seder begins, inform everyone that Uncle Max (or Grandma Rose) has a small treat for any child who asks a Passover question.

✡ Vary the songs at the seder. Perhaps your children learn Passover songs at school, or you could check online for simple songs with familiar tunes.

✡ During the seder, ask everyone present to close her or his eyes, picture what freedom looks like, and give a one-word description. As an alternative, ask each person to name something wonderful that happened in the past year.

✡ Jewish holidays are important times to think of others. In this spirit, when shopping for Passover groceries, encourage your children to choose an item to give to a local food bank or homeless shelter.